Mr. Cthulhu Presents.

COLORING BOOK
Illustrations by Phil Velikan

Cthulhu's Coloring Book & Necronomicon of Sunny Day Doings

Layout, cover and illustrations by Phil Velikan www.FindPhil.com
Edited by Holly Kondras. Thanks Holly!

Printed in the United States of America

Published by VIG Publishing 1st printing 2015, 2nd edition 2018

IN HIS HOUSE AT R'LYEH, DEAD CTHULHU WAITS DREAMING.
YET HE SHALL RISE AND HIS KINGDOM SHALL COVER THE EARTH.

-THE NECRONOMICON

A little history:

This book is an update to the book of the same name. I redid the cover and added 16 pages to get it in line with my *Monsters and Cryptids of America* coloring book and future books in the series. If you bought the first version, THANK YOU! I hope my additions are of value. Please review my books on Amazon as this helps their ranking on the lists! :)

Howard Phillips Lovecraft (1890-1937) wrote many stories centered around the Cthulhu mythology, starting with *The Call of Cthulhu* in 1928. He went on to write six more short stories that built on the legends and lore of his creation – none of which were especially successful during his lifetime.

The Dunwich Horror, 1929

The Whisperer in Darkness, 1931

At the Mountains of Madness, 1936

The Shadow Over Innsmouth, 1936

The Shadow Out of Time, 1936

The Haunter of the Dark, 1936

A few of the stories enjoyed moderate success, so he was encouraged to develop his own universe of horror and macabre stories dealing with elder gods, deities from space and the bottom of the seas – all of which can be traced back to *The Call of Cthulhu*. He achieved a cult status in his day and made enough to live on, but did not achieve the fame he craved until well after his death. In recent decades he has become ranked as an equal to Edgar Allen Poe in American fantasy and horror writing. Like Poe, most of his stories are in the public domain and can be found online for free. Search him out, you'll be glad you did.

BYAKHEE

"There flapped rhythmically a horde of tame, trained, hybrid winged things ... not altogether crows, nor moles, nor buzzards, nor ants, nor decomposed human beings, but something I cannot and must not recall."

— H.P. Lovecraft, *The Festival*

A-Maze-ing
Help our mascot, Mr. Cthulhu find his way
thru the maze of aeons to the 21st century!

Mr. Cthulhu

2025!

MOONBEAST

"For they were not men at all, or even approximately men, but great greyish-white slippery things which could expand and contract at will, and whose principal shape - though it often changed - was that of a sort of toad without any eyes, but with a curious vibrating mass of short pink tentacles on the end of its blunt, vague snout."

— H.P. Lovecraft, *Dream-Quest Of Unknown Kadath*

Dot-to-dot

Follow the dots to find something "Not of this world" named Kassogtha and color him.

10
11
12
9
42
19
18
17
8
13
41
20
16
14
7
15
40
21
39
22
6
38
23
37
5
24
36
25
4
26
27
35
34
28
3
33
29
32
2
30
1
31

DEEP ONE

"I think their predominant colour was a greyish-green, though they had white bellies. They were mostly shiny and slippery, but the ridges of their backs were scaly. Their forms vaguely suggested the anthropoid, while their heads were the heads of fish, with prodigious bulging eyes that never closed. At the sides of their necks were palpitating gills, and their long paws were webbed. They hopped irregularly, sometimes on two legs and sometimes on four."

— H.P. Lovecraft, *The Shadow Over Innsmouth*

Word puzzle

Put the words below into the grid and then unscramble the boxed letters to find a Lovecraftian beastie you can color somewhere in this book.

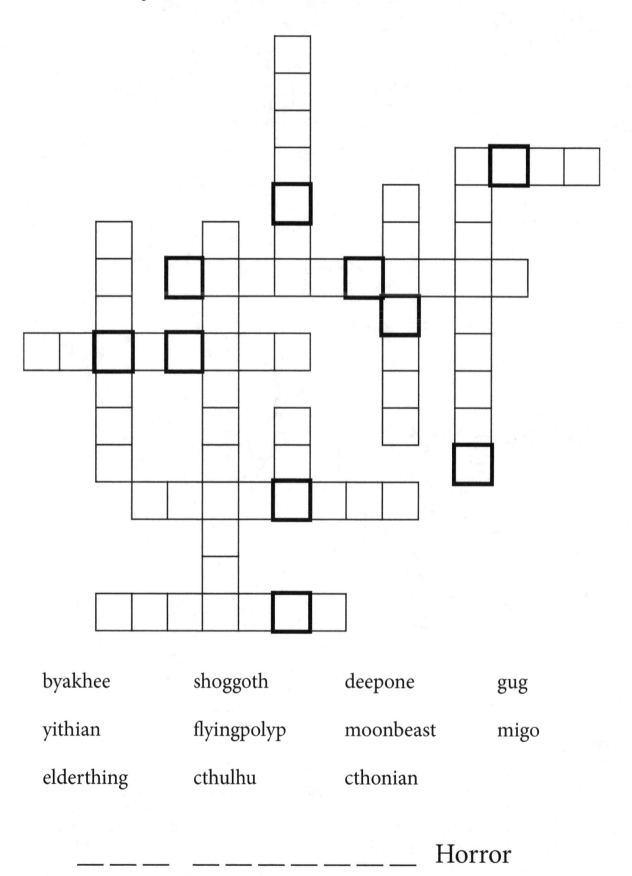

byakhee   shoggoth   deepone   gug

yithian   flyingpolyp   moonbeast   migo

elderthing   cthulhu   cthonian

__ __ __   __ __ __ __ __ __ __ Horror

CTHULHU

"It seemed to be a sort of monster, or symbol representing a monster, of a form which only a diseased fancy could conceive. If I say that my somewhat extravagant imagination yielded simultaneous pictures of an octopus, a dragon, and a human caricature, I shall not be unfaithful to the spirit of the thing. A pulpy, tentacled head surmounted a grotesque and scaly body with rudimentary wings;"

— H.P. Lovecraft, *The Call Of Cthulhu*

Window into Madness

The top grid has been placed with elder signs to stop the madness, cross out the blocks in the lower grid to find the words hidden in the madness. The first one has been done for you.

l	a	o	e	v	e	a	a	g	c	a	r	a	a	a	f	g	t	a
a	c	a	g	t	a	h	o	a	n	a	g	a	i	a	a	n	a	s
a	g	a	d	a	e	a	a	e	a	p	a	r	o	a	n	e	a	s
e	a	l	d	a	e	a	a	r	a	a	g	a	o	e	a	d	s	a
n	e	i	g	a	h	t	a	a	g	a	a	u	a	n	t	e	a	a
a	o	e	c	c	a	r	a	u	l	a	t	i	a	s	a	u	t	s
a	s	u	h	a	o	a	a	g	a	e	a	g	o	a	t	a	e	h
t	a	c	h	a	e	o	a	a	t	c	e	h	a	o	s	a	u	a
i	y	a	o	g	a	s	e	o	t	h	a	a	o	e	t	h	a	a
m	a	o	o	d	a	n	a	a	b	a	e	a	a	s	e	t	a	a
a	e	g	a	n	a	e	a	o	r	a	e	r	i	a	a	d	a	a

Cthulhu's Coloring Book and Necronomicon of Sunny Day Doings ©2018 VIGpublishing

HUNTING HORROR

"The Nodens raised a howl of triumph when Nyarlathotep, close on his quarry, stopped, baffled by a glare that seared his hunting-horrors* to grey dust."

— H.P. Lovecraft, *Dream-Quest Of Unknown Kadath*

*Flying vipers with great black rubbery wings, distorted heads, and arms ending in monstrous claws.

Bathtime!!
Draw yourself having fun in the tub with Dagon!

ELDER THING

"Objects are eight feet long all over with a six-foot five-ridged barrel torso. Dark grey, flexible, and infinitely tough. Seven-foot membraneous wings of same colour, found folded, spread out of furrows between ridges. The blunt bulbous neck holds a yellowish five-pointed star-fish-shaped head. At end of each tube is a spherical expansion where the yellowish membrane rolls back to reveal a glassy, red-irised globe, evidently an eye."

— H.P. Lovecraft, *At the Mountains of Madness*

Another maze?
Cool, mazes are fun.
Help the Gug find his toothbrush

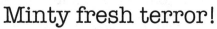

Minty fresh terror!

GUG

"After it came another paw, and after that a great black-furred arm to which both of the paws were attached by short forearms. Then two pink eyes shone, and the head of the awakened gug sentry, large as a barrel, wabbled into view. The eyes jutted two inches from each side, shaded by bony protuberances overgrown with coarse hairs. But the head was chiefly terrible because of the mouth, opening vertically instead of horizontally."

— H.P. Lovecraft, *Dream-Quest Of Unknown Kadath*

Soduku of Doom
Place the numbers 1-4 in each column and row without duplicating them!

Grid 1 (top left):

1	3		
		1	3
4			

Grid 2 (top right):

	1		3
	2		
3			1

Grid 3 (bottom left):

1		3	
		1	
2			3
	3		

Grid 4 (bottom right):

	1	3	
			3
	2	1	

FLYING POLYP

"...the basis of the fear was a horrible elder race of half-polypous, utterly alien entities which had come through space from immeasurably distant universes. There were veiled suggestions of a monstrous plasticity, and of temporary lapses of visibility."

— H.P. Lovecraft, *The Shadow Out Of Time*

Numbered **Color out of space**
Color the idol using the color chart below

1-red
2-green
3-blue
4-yellow
5-black

YITHIAN

"The Great Race's members were immense rugose cones ten feet high, and with head and other organs attached to foot-thick, distensible limbs spreading from the apexes. They spoke by the clicking or scraping of huge claws attached to the end of their limbs, and walked by the expansion and contraction of the rubbery, grey substance on their base."

— H.P. Lovecraft, *The Shadow Out Of Time*

Five Pointed Star

Start at 5 and count by 5s to get to 100 percent Elder sign protection!

2	5	67	98	32	09
85	10	15	27	43	79
1	8	20	89	93	62
36	97	25	30	35	40
51	23	23	41	47	45
43	53	14	84	55	50
15	21	32	65	60	10
56	18	67	70	15	8
42	79	80	75	32	97
91	90	85	22	87	23
29	95	16	24	92	53
32	100	73	11	18	21

2	54	5	98	32	09
85	67	10	27	43	79
1	8	15	20	93	62
36	97	32	25	30	10
51	23	23	41	35	46
43	55	50	45	40	78
15	60	32	61	63	92
56	65	70	76	15	8
42	79	75	72	32	97
91	50	80	85	87	23
29	92	16	90	95	53
32	16	73	11	100	21

Nyarlathotep (god of a thousand forms)

"the rats seemed determined to lead me on, even unto those grinning caverns of earth's centre where Nyarlathotep, the mad faceless god, howls blindly to the piping of two amorphous idiot flute-players."

— H.P. Lovecraft, *The Rats in The Walls*

Occult Secrets

Follow the lines from each number to find the letter (or symbol) that goes in the corresponding spot below to find the titles of two frightening Lovecraft stories.

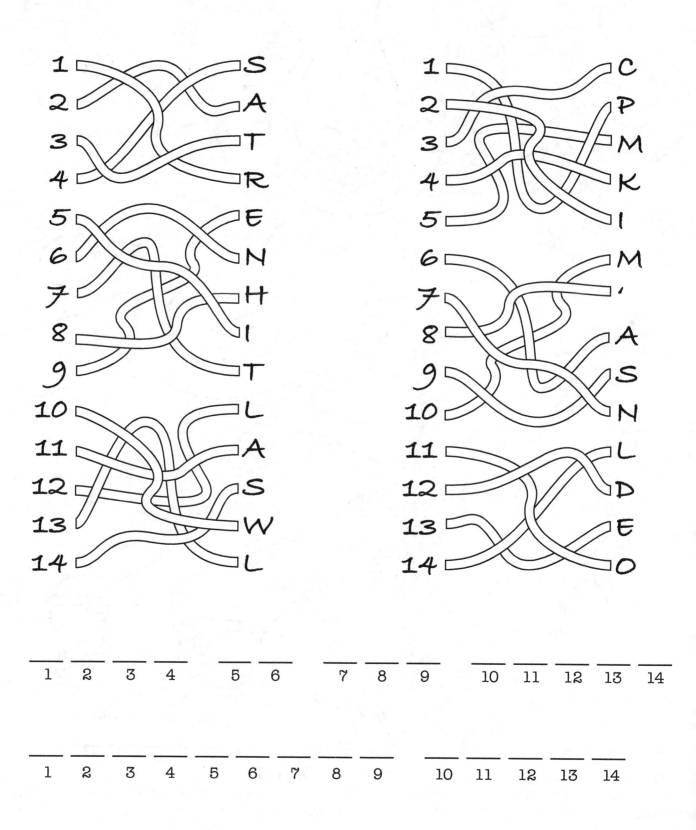

1 ___ 2 ___ 3 ___ 4 ___   5 ___ 6 ___   7 ___ 8 ___ 9 ___   10 ___ 11 ___ 12 ___ 13 ___ 14 ___

1 ___ 2 ___ 3 ___ 4 ___ 5 ___ 6 ___ 7 ___ 8 ___ 9 ___   10 ___ 11 ___ 12 ___ 13 ___ 14 ___

SHOGGOTH

"They were normally shapeless entities composed of a viscous jelly which looked like an agglutination of bubbles, and each averaged about fifteen feet in diameter when a sphere. They had, however, a constantly shifting shape and volume - throwing out temporary developments or forming apparent organs of sight, hearing, and speech in imitation of their masters, either spontaneously or according to suggestion."

— H.P. Lovecraft, *At the Mountains Of Madness*

Everyone loves a good book
Color the Necronomicon

Night Gaunt

"Uncouth black things with smooth, oily, whale-like surfaces, bat wings whose beating made no sound, ugly prehensile paws, and barbed tails that lashed needlessly and disquietingly. And worst of all, they had no faces, but only a suggestive blankness where a face ought to be. All they ever did was clutch and fly and tickle; that was the way of night-gaunts."

— H.P. Lovecraft, *Dream-Quest Of Unknown Kadath*

Weird word search
You know what to do.

```
A  C  S  D  A  T  U  R  F  Q  S  H  A  C
W  D  H  O  L  E  S  F  T  I  A  D  S  W
Y  K  A  I  U  D  A  C  H  I  Z  W  K  H
F  J  S  A  C  R  U  L  A  T  R  E  A  F
T  A  T  Q  Z  H  T  A  H  H  A  L  Y  A
A  T  U  A  L  M  A  C  A  A  A  L  U  I
W  I  R  U  R  I  W  K  D  Q  Z  E  S  Y
F  K  H  R  F  S  S  Q  U  U  T  R  L  C
A  T  A  A  Z  K  O  I  N  A  Z  E  E  A
C  C  R  S  Y  A  V  A  W  R  W  A  I  D
A  T  F  H  S  T  E  T  I  A  H  D  A  T
S  A  W  A  L  O  V  E  C  R  A  F  T  D
Q  H  T  U  U  N  G  A  H  F  T  A  S  H
W  D  U  F  K  I  G  T  S  O  E  T  H  I
R  L  Y  E  H  C  F  C  H  Y  L  Q  U  R
I  C  D  Z  R  T  G  T  H  A  Y  C  Z  A
```

Cthulhu	Alhazred	Kassogtha
Lovecraft	Rlyeh	Ithaqua
Whately	Dweller	Hastur
Miskatonic	Dunwich	Dholes

Pickman's Model

"Pickman's morbid art was pre-eminently one of demoniac portraiture. These figures were seldom completely human, but often approached humanity in varying degree. Most of the bodies, while roughly bipedal, had a forward slumping, and a vaguely canine cast. The texture of the majority was a kind of unpleasant rubberiness."

— H.P. Lovecraft, *Pickman's Model*

Maze-tastic!
Help the Wamp get to his home.

WAMP

"The steed was quite dead, with its blood all sucked away through a singular wound in its throat."

— H.P. Lovecraft, *Dream-Quest Of Unknown Kadath*

The wamp haunts ancient ruins, graveyards and abandoned cities. It has a pale sphere body splashed with red, webbed feet, nine legs and head with no eyes, bat-like ears and a wrinkled snout.

Yig's Mystery Grid Image

Fill in the blocks according to the coordinates below. The first one is done for you.

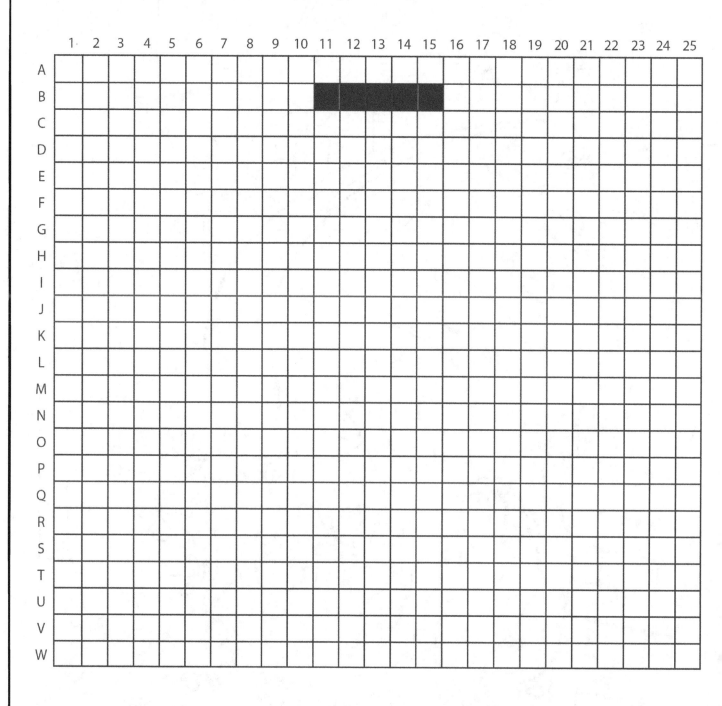

B 11-15

C 8-10, 16-18

D 7,19

E 6, 20

F 5, 21

G 4, 8, 9, 17, 18, 22

H 4, 7, 10, 16, 19, 22

I 4, 6, 11, 15, 20, 22

J 4, 6, 11, 15, 20, 22

K 4, 6, 11, 15, 20, 22

L 4, 7-10, 16-19, 22

M 5, 21

N 6, 12, 14, 20

O 7, 19

P 3, 8, 18, 23

Q 2, 7, 9, 10, 12, 14, 16, 17, 19, 24

R 2, 6, 11, 13, 15, 20, 24

S 3, 5, 10, 13, 16, 21, 23

T 4, 9, 12, 14, 17, 22

U 6, 8, 11, 15, 18, 20

V 7, 12, 16, 19

Cthulhu's Coloring Book and Necronomicon of Sunny Day Doings ©2018 VIGpublishing

Yig

"A semi-anthropomorphic serpent, I did quite readily place as a prototype of the Yig, Quetzal-coatl, and Kukulcan the feathered serpent."

— H.P. Lovecraft, *The Mound*

Crypt-oquip

Each letter below stands for another letter. You must replace them starting with the hints given, to discover the Lovecraft quote. Write the replaced letters below the sentences.

The F stands for the letter A, D=E and Q=N

JAFJ GE QBJ LDFL RAGKA KFQ DJDMQFS SGD, FQL RGJA EJMFQVD
_ A _ _   _ _   _ N _   _ E A _   _ _ _ _ _   _ _ _   _ _ _ _ _ _ _   _ _ _ ,   _ _ _   _ _ _ _   _ _ _ _ _ _ _

FDBQE DZDQ LDFJA WFX LGD. "JAD QFWDSDEE KGJX"
_ _ _ _ _   _ _ _ _   _ _ _ _ _   _ _ _   _ _ _ .   " _ _ _   _ _ _ _ _ _ _ _   _ _ _ _ "

J stands for the letter A, M=O, and C=F

"BLD MQPDKB JEP KBHMETDKB DZMBVME MC ZJESVEP VK CDJH, JEP BLD
" _ _ _   _ _ _ _ _ _   _ _ _   _ _ _ _ _ _ _ _   _ _ _ _ _ _   _ _   _ _ _ _ _ _ _   _ _   _ _ _ _ ,   _ _ _   _ _ _

MQPDKB JEP KBHMETDKB SVEP MC CDJH VK CDJH MC BLD YESEMAE."
_ _ _ _ _ _   _ _ _   _ _ _ _ _ _ _ _   _ _ _ _   _ _   _ _ _ _   _ _   _ _ _ _   _ _   _ _ _   _ _ _ _ _ _ ."

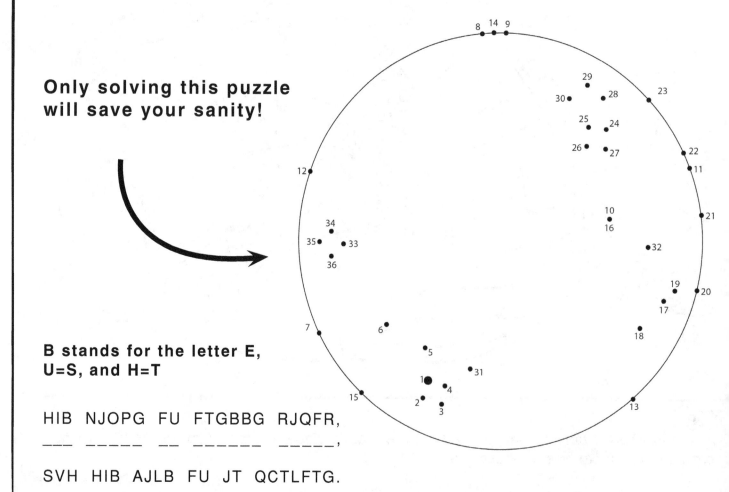

Only solving this puzzle will save your sanity!

B stands for the letter E, U=S, and H=T

HIB NJOPG FU FTGBBG RJQFR,
_ _ _   _ _ _ _ _   _ _   _ _ _ _ _ _   _ _ _ _ _ ,

SVH HIB AJLB FU JT QCTLFTG.
_ _ _   _ _ _   _ _ _ _   _ _   _ _   _ _ _ _ _ _ _ .

MI-GO

"They were pinkish things about five feet long; with crustaceous bodies bearing vast pairs of dorsal fins or membranous wings and several sets of articulated limbs, and with a sort of convoluted ellipsoid, covered with multitudes of very short antennae, where a head would ordinarily be."

— H.P. Lovecraft, *The Whisperer In Darkness*

Dot-to-dot

Be careful that you don't cut yourself when working this puzzle. Things could get uncomfortable with Alach-Nacha!

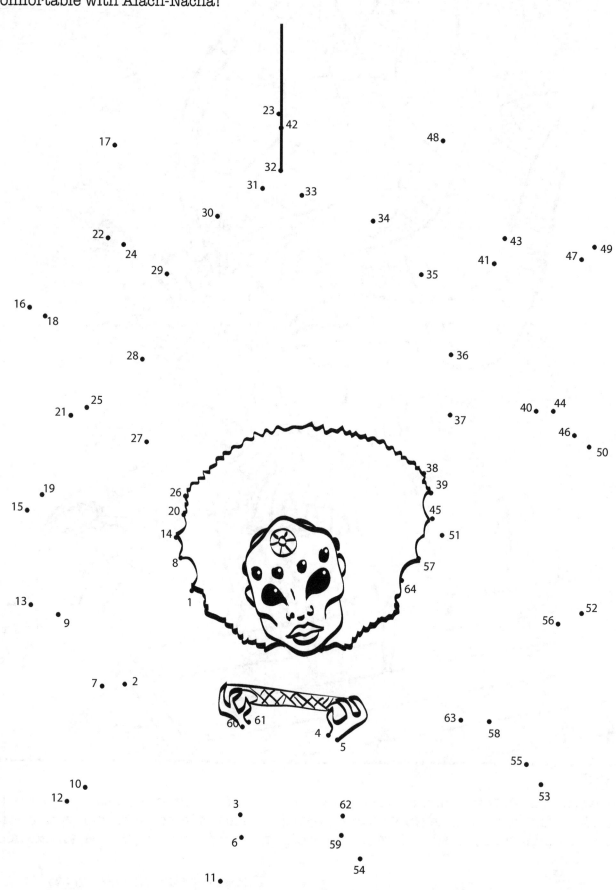

Cthulhu's Coloring Book and Necronomicon of Sunny Day Doings ©2018 VIGpublishing

Brown Jenkin

"That object—no larger than a good-sized rat and quaintly called by the townspeople "Brown Jenkin" – had long hair and the shape of a rat, but that its sharp-toothed, bearded face was evilly human while its paws were like tiny human hands. Its voice was a kind of loathsome titter, and it could speak all languages. "

— H.P. Lovecraft, The Dreams in the *Witch House*

Puzzles of pain

Start at the arrow and count around the circle, writing the letter in the spaces below.

Start here and write down every 3rd letter

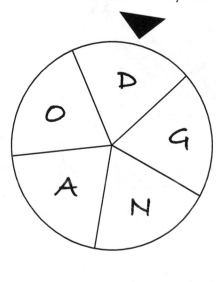

_ _ _ _ _

Write down every 3rd letter

_ _ _ _ _ _ _

Write down every 3rd letter

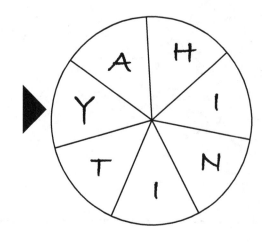

_ _ _ _ _ _

Write down every 5th letter

_ _ _ _ _ _ _ _ _ _ _ _

A-Mazement!
Help the deep ones find their way home.

T M H T H ! M N

N
P
E
O
P
O
E
E

Find the square to the right in the top image. Then write down the letter that meets it in the left column, and the letter that meets it in the top row. Do all six for a message from the Elder Thing.

_ _ _ _ _ _ _ _ _ _ _ _

Crazy Cultist Calling

Design a crest for the robe of the cultist to show which monster he is trying to call forth.

Color the town a cheery shade of DOOM.

Let Cthulhu tell the world what's buggin' you! Fill in the word balloon with your gripes.

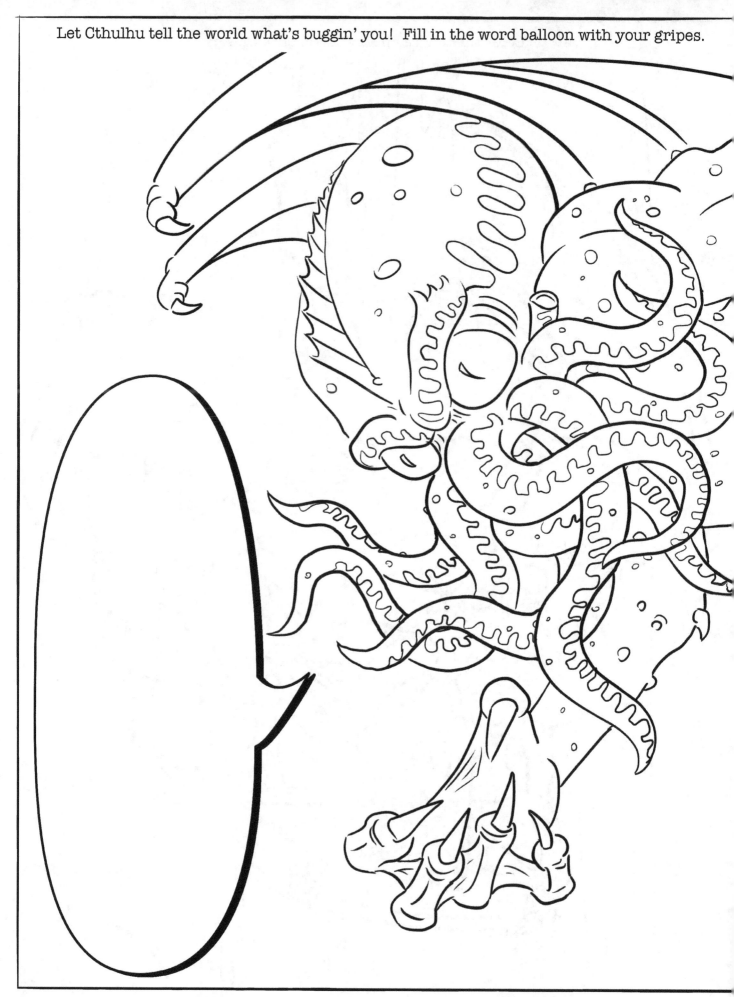

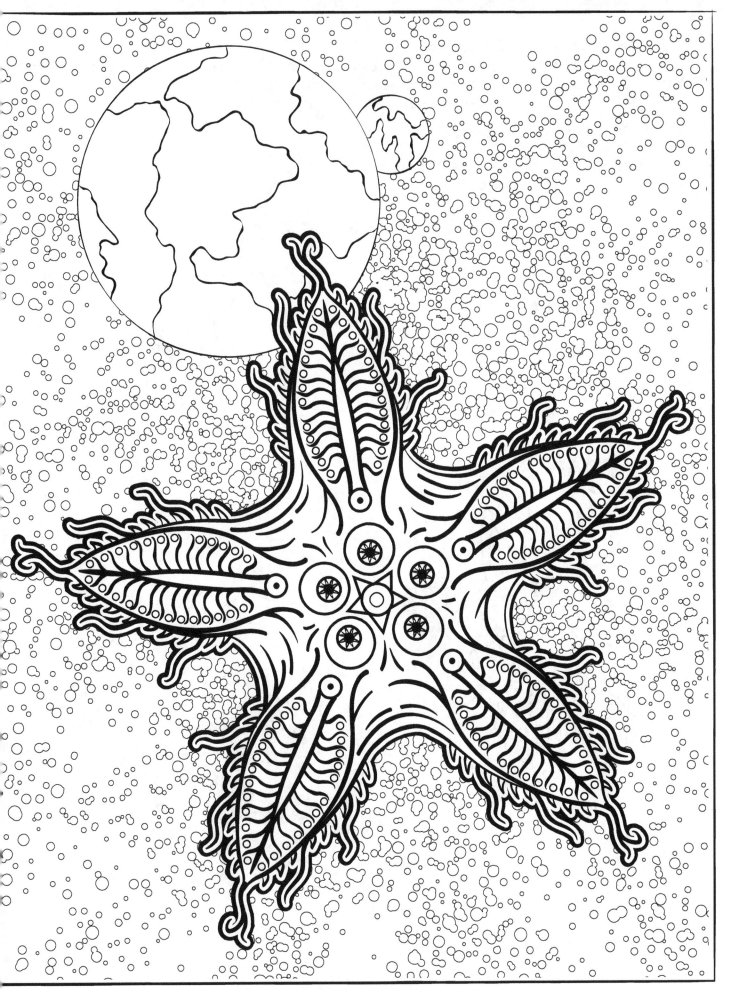

Maddening Adornments

These are the untouched images from the last book. One of the exciting aspects of them was that they had no backgrounds. With a little imagination and tape, you could make all sorts of things. We are including them here in a smaller size for you to do just that.

Photocopy the following pages and make your own battle for the universe. An army of shoggoths, a ground unit of unspeakable horrors, a flock of byakhee and hunting horrors hanging from your ceiling, the possibilities are endless.

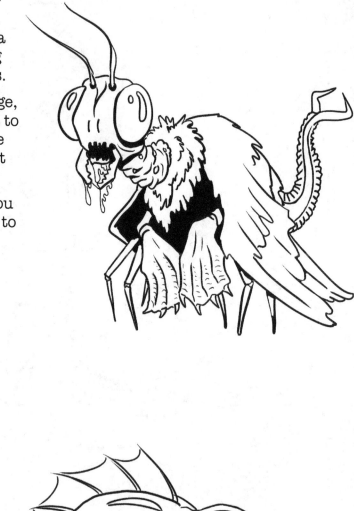

If your photocopier or scanner can flip the page, print out a flipped image, cut it out and glue it to the back of one that you colored. You will have a two sided horror for a mobile or stick puppet play on how the universe will end or began!

Please post a picture on our amazon page if you use these in some awesome project. We'd love to see them! Oh, and review the book please. It helps our ranking on Amazon.

Cthulhu's Coloring Book and Necronomicon of Sunny Day Doings ©2018 VIGpublishing

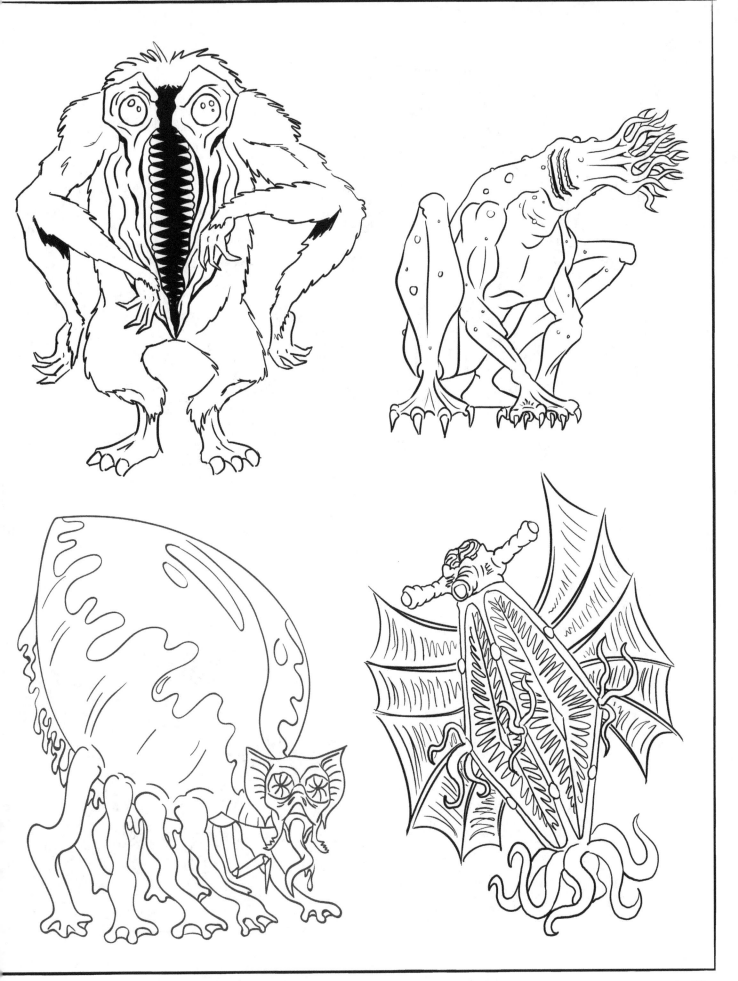

Answer key

0.

THE HUNTING Horror

12.
- Lovecraft
- Cthonian
- Deep ones
- Elder gods
- Nightgaunt
- Occultists
- Shoggoth
- Tcho tchos
- Yog sothoth
- Moonbeast
- Gnorri

16.

1	3	2	4
2	4	1	3
3	2	4	1
4	1	3	2

2	1	4	3
4	3	2	1
1	2	3	4
3	4	2	1

1	4	3	2
3	2	1	4
2	1	4	3
4	3	2	1

4	1	3	2
2	3	4	1
1	4	2	3
3	2	1	4

4. Rats in the walls   Pickman's model

8.

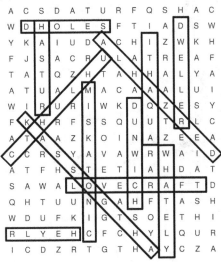

32.

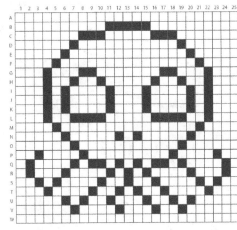

 34.
That is not dead which can eternal lie, and with strange aeons even death may die. "The Nameless City"

The oldest and strongest emotion of mankind is fear and the oldest and strongest kind of fear is fear of the unknown.

The world is indeed comic, but the joke is on mankind.

8.
agon, Cthulhu, Yithian, Necronomicon

42.
ET (Elder Thing) phone home!

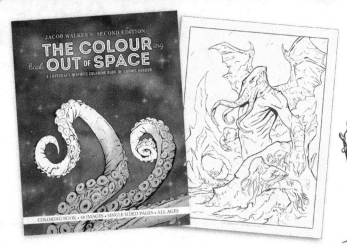

Ohio 1955-1972

A sample coloring page of Ohio's Loveland Frogs, from our second book, titled *Mr. Cthulhu Presents: Monsters and Cryptids in the United States of America*. On sale now on Amazon.com!

A sample coloring page Of West Virginia's Flatwoods Monster from the *Mr. Cthulhu Presents: Space Aliens and Flying Objects in the United States of America.* Coming to Amazon.com in 2018.

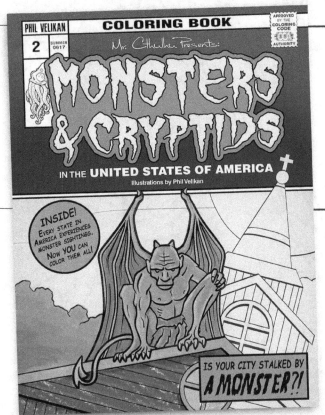

CPSIA information can be obtained
at www.ICGtesting.com
Printed in the USA
LVHW02s1016201018
594197LV00007B/15/P